HPS 1484

JAMES MACMILLAN

SERAPH

FOR TRUMPET & STRING ORCHESTRA

Boosey & Hawkes Music Publishers Ltd
www.boosey.com

Published by Boosey & Hawkes Music Publishers Ltd
Aldwych House
71–91 Aldwych
London
WC2B 4HN

www.boosey.com

© Copyright 2010 by Boosey & Hawkes Music Publishers Ltd

ISMN 979-0-060-12545-4
ISBN 978-0-85162-820-2
HPS 1484

First impression 2013

Printed in England by The Halstan Printing Group, Amersham, Bucks

Music origination by The Note Factory

Contents

Commissioned by The Scottish Ensemble and Perth Concert Hall
with the support of the PRS for Music Foundation and The Radcliffe Trust

Seraph was composed in 2010. The first performance was given on
17 February 2011 at Wigmore Hall, London, by Alison Balsom (trumpet)
and the Scottish Ensemble, Jonathan Morton (leader).

A recording of the first performance is available on
EMI Classics 50999 6 78590 2 3.

Duration: 15 minutes

Trumpet part with piano reduction available on sale
(ISMN 979-0-060-12346-7, ISBN 978-0-85162-782-3)
Performance materials available on hire

to Alison Balsom

SERAPH

JAMES MACMILLAN
(b 1959)

I

19199

2

5

19199

II

12

14

III

16

22

24

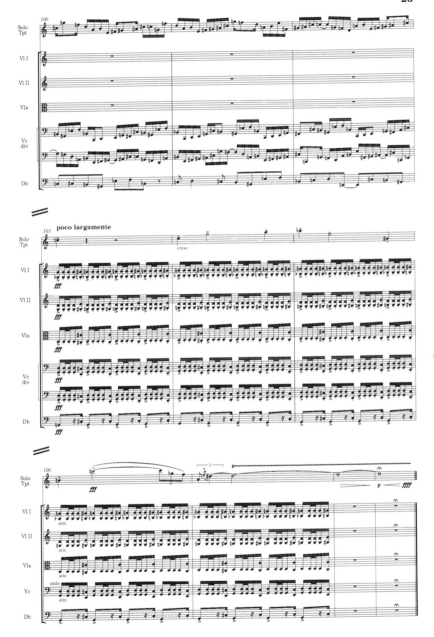

SELECTED SCORES

A complete list of our extensive library of classic 20th-century
scores is available on request. For more information about
Boosey & Hawkes composers visit our website

Béla BARTÓK
Concerto for Orchestra
Piano Concerto no 3
Violin Concertos nos 1 & 2
Divertimento
Sonata for 2 Pianos and Percussion

Leonard BERNSTEIN
Candide
Chichester Psalms
West Side Story

Benjamin BRITTEN
Les Illuminations
Peter Grimes
Serenade for Tenor, Horn and Strings
War Requiem
Young Person's Guide to the Orchestra

Aaron COPLAND
Appalachian Spring Suite
Billy the Kid Suite
Quiet City
El Salon Mexico

Frederick DELIUS
Appalachia
Sea Drift

Edward ELGAR
Pomp and Circumstance Marches
Sea Pictures
Cockaigne Overture

Alberto GINASTERA
Dances from Estancia
Variaciones Concertantes

Bohuslav MARTINŮ
Double Concerto
Symphonies nos 1–6

Serge PROKOFIEFF
The Love of Three Oranges
Piano Concertos nos 2, 3 & 5
Violin Concertos nos 1 & 2
Peter and the Wolf

Serge RACHMANINOFF
The Bells
Piano Concertos nos 1–4
Rhapsody on a Theme of Paganini
Symphonic Dances
Symphonies nos 2 & 3

Richard STRAUSS
Elektra
Salome
Four Last Songs
Der Rosenkavalier

Igor STRAVINSKY
Oedipus Rex
Pétrouchka
The Rake's Progress
The Rite of Spring
Symphony of Psalms

BOOSEY & HAWKES

AN IMAGEM COMPANY